How to care for your horse

by Janet L Eley, BVSc MRCVS.

Sponsored by
Strongid* Caramel

HENSTON

* Trade Mark

Henston Veterinary Publications
Veterinary Business Development Ltd
Olympus House, Werrington Centre
Peterborough PE4 6NA

Telephone: 01733 325522
e-mail: henston@vetsonline.com

Designed and produced by Veterinary Business Development

Printed by Page Bros, Norwich, Norfolk

ISBN: 1 85054 154 6

First edition

© 1999 Veterinary Business Development Ltd

Price: £7.50

Contents

Foreword

The *Henston* Veterinary Publications editorial team is very grateful to Janet for her input and patience during the protracted gestation of this book. We hope you will appreciate her down-to-earth, common sense approach and that its contents will prove to be a constant source of reassurance and practical advice.

David Watson, BVetMed, MRCVS.
Editor.

Acknowledgements

The author and publishers gratefully acknowledge the support of Pfizer (UK) Ltd, the makers of Strongid* Caramel, who have generously sponsored production of this first edition.

*Trade Mark

Dedication

To my god-daughter KATY

Chapter 1
Preparing for horse ownership

- **Commitment**
- **Cost**
- **Accommodation**
- **Vetting for purchase, Warranties and Receipt**
- **Insurance**
- **Documents**
- **Equipment**
- **Transport**
- **Register with veterinary and farriery practices**

Commitment

Once you have purchased a horse you are responsible for the care of that animal on a daily basis. You must have a basic knowledge of horse, stable and pasture management and sufficient time to look after the horse, the equipment and its environment. If you do not have the time or necessary knowledge to personally care for the horse you must be able to afford a full time groom or place the animal at full livery at a reputable stables. If you are in any doubt that you can provide adequate care you should not consider horse ownership. There are many courses available on horse care and stable management as well as books, videos and leaflets for novice and experienced horse owners.

Cost

Horses are expensive animals both to purchase and to maintain. Many first time purchasers can afford the initial cost of a horse, which may be the tip of the iceberg, but are unaware of all the others expenses involved.

● *Equipment*

This includes a headcollar with a lead rope; a saddle with girth, stirrup leathers and irons and a numnah; a bridle with a bit. Some animals need exercise boots and horses doing road work should wear knee boots. Rugs, bandages and travel wear may be needed. A basic grooming kit, a tack cleaning kit and a first aid kit all add to the initial costs.

● *Rent*

You must pay rent for grazing and stabling or the upkeep and repair of your own facilities e.g. fencing. Rates on horse stables and ancillary buildings have to be calculated as well as the additional water and electricity costs.

● *Fees*

Annual veterinary fees for routine procedures like worming, vaccinations, dental care, and the unforeseen cost of treatment for any ailments or accidental injuries.

● *Farriery visits*

Farriery visits are required every 4 to 6 weeks for foot trimming and shoeing.

● *Bedding material and disposal of manure.*

You will need somewhere to store bedding material. Some animals cannot be bedded on straw, which is relatively cheap compared to the alternatives like rubber flooring, shavings, paper or hemp.

● *Feed*

The amount and type of additional feed needed depends on the quality and quantity of grass available and the age, weight and condition of the horse. The amount and type of exercise the horse does may also mean a basic forage diet will need supplementing with concentrates.

Feed buckets, mangers, hay nets and feed bins are required. If hay is purchased in bulk (which is cheaper) you will need a feed store or hay barn.

- *Additional costs*

Additional costs may include riding instruction, schooling the horse, hiring a menage, competition fees, registration fees, transportation, clipping and wages for a groom or livery charges.

- *Insurance*

Third party public liability insurance is needed in case your animal damages property or injures another person. There is health insurance to cover veterinary bills, loss of use and accidental death or humane destruction. The financial cost of the animal and its athletic use reflects the type of cover required and the cost of the policy.

The tack and equipment can be covered against theft or damage. Trailers and horse boxes also require insurance cover.

Accommodation

It is wise to arrange accommodation for your horse prior to purchase and not wait until the animal arrives on your doorstep!

If you have your own land make sure that it is adequately fenced for an equine. Native ponies should not be grazed on lush cattle pasture. Access to grass may be limited by stabling the animal for part of the day or by judicious use of electric fencing. The paddocks should be free of farm equipment, rubbish and poisonous plants and other hazards. See Appendix 3. A field shelter or good natural shelter should be provided. Although many ponies and horses can live out all year round many have to be stabled in inclement weather conditions or if they are ill or injured. Most competition animals and those in hard work are stabled at times. Some livery yards only provide limited grazing facilities or turn out paddocks so animals kept at these premises spend many hours in a stable and therefore require hay or an alternative form of forage at regular intervals throughout the day. Often in the winter when fields become "poached" or waterlogged the horses are not allowed on the pasture They have to be taken out of the stable to be exercised each day. The livery stables may provide full care of your horse (full livery) or you may be totally responsible for it (DIY livery). It is wise to have a written agreement if you are renting grazing and stabling, so both parties understand the conditions and financial arrangement. The type of accommodation offered may not be suitable for all breeds of horse. See Appendix 4 (Guidelines for the operation of livery yards BHS publication). If you hope to convert existing buildings or plan new stabling, do get expert advice before starting on the work.

Vetting for purchase

It is wise to have any horse you wish to buy examined by an equine veterinary surgeon prior to purchase. The five stage examination should be carried out according to the recommended procedure advised by the RCVS/BVA and a certificate provided. Normally blood samples are taken to test for drugs which the vendor may have given the horse to conceal a problem.

The veterinary surgeon will advise you on the suitability of the horse for purchase for a particular use. It is well worth attending the veterinary examination: you will learn how to examine a horse in a systematic way, and how to recognise common problems. You are also on hand to discuss any ailment the veterinary surgeon has found during the examination. As a novice horse owner you will be purchasing a trained, adult horse that may have a few minor defects not necessarily affecting its performance.

Warranties should be in writing and cover any matters which are important to the purchaser. These normally include the temperament of the animal, athletic ability, behaviour and suitability. The purchaser may want an animal that is good to box, shoe, clip, catch and in traffic. These conditions are added to the warranty. A warranty is not the responsibility of the veterinary surgeon; it is between the vendor and the purchaser. If in any doubt ask a solicitor for legal advice in drawing up the document.

A receipt should be obtained from the vendor at the time of purchase. The vendor may be the owner or the agent of the owner; where possible get the owner's address. Remember many horses are stolen to sell on and if you buy stolen property you will lose the animal and your money. If you leave a deposit on an animal make sure you have a receipt for the deposit and that it is returnable if the horse does not "pass" the veterinary inspection.

Insurance

Insurance should be arranged prior to removing the horse from the vendor's care. Horses can be injured in transit to their new home so make sure you have adequate cover from day one. Insurance brokers and other horse owners will be able to point you in the direction of a reputable insurance company. The cheapest policy is rarely the best. Medical insurance does not cover ailments that are present at the inception of the policy. The insurance company may need a veterinary certificate prior to insuring the animal. Some companies accept the vetting for purchase certificate for this purpose while others require a different examination and certificate. As the new owner of the horse you are responsible for paying for any examinations or certificates. Insurance companies do not normally insure animals that have already been the subject of a loss of use claim. These animals should have a brand mark to identify them. (Imported horses have a different brand).

Documents

The horse may have a vaccination record card, a life height certificate, or be registered with a breed society or an athletic performance association. If the vendor states that any of these documents exist, do obtain all the documents when you pay for the horse. Check any brands or registration documents for authenticity. Make sure the documents are for the correct horse and check the identification drawings carefully. If in any doubt contact the official body who authorised the certificate before you hand over any money.

Equipment

Horses are often sold with some basic equipment such as a head-collar or rug. A bridle is a necessity in order to safely lead the horse in a controlled manner. Expensive items like the saddle can sometimes be purchased with the horse but are not normally included in the price of the horse. Second-hand English leather tack in good condition may be bought from a reputable saddler or tack outlet. If your horse is a little thin or rather fat there is no point in buying a new saddle until the animal is the correct size! Saddles, bridles and rugs must all fit correctly otherwise they may cause injuries to the horse. Dirty or damaged tack can cause pressure sores and wounds e.g. saddle sores and girth galls. The saddle also has to be the right size for the rider. Some items of equipment are not needed immediately and can be purchased after the horse has arrived home. If the horse is clipped out or normally rugged obviously you will need rugs from day one. If possible try to buy the rugs with the horse providing they are in good condition and reasonably priced. Second hand rugs and numnahs from an unknown source may be infected with ringworm and other contagious diseases and should be cleaned with a broad spectrum antibacterial and fungicidal agent . Your veterinary surgeon can advise you on the correct product to use.

Transport

If you do not own your own trailer or horsebox you will have to arrange for the vendor or a commercial horse transport company to deliver your horse. It is worth checking that the horse will travel in both trailers and boxes as some animals are only used to one mode of transport. Make sure the horse is being transported in a vehicle which is insured and in good condition. Insist that the horse wears the correct protective travelling gear e.g. poll guard, tail guard, travel boots and rug. This may mean that you have to provide the gear and fit it yourself before the journey. Check that your horse insurance covers the horse for the journey. You may think this is a bit "over the top" but many horses are injured in transit, loading and unloading e.g. accidental injuries to unprotected legs.

Register with a veterinary and farriery practice

Check with the local horse practice that they are happy to provide the veterinary care for your horse or find out which practice covers the work at your livery stables. The British Equine Veterinary Association or the RCVS will provide a list of practices in your area. If you are purchasing a horse locally you may be able to use the veterinary surgeon and farrier who already attend to it. A farrier will be required every 4 to 6 weeks so it is important to make sure you are on a farrier's list before you become a horse owner. All farriers must by law have a current registration certificate in order to shoe horses. The Farriers Registration Council publishes a list of all registered farriers (Appendix 4). It is illegal to allow an unregistered person to shoe your horse, so always check that you are employing a professional farrier: the horse's welfare is at stake.

When you are satisfied that all the preparations have been made, ask the vendor for information on any aspect of the horse's present management system which you are not sure of e.g.. bedding material, diet, likes and dislikes, worming programme, previous ailments, exercise routine, so that the change of ownership is stress free for the horse (and yourself). Hopefully, if you choose the right horse for your capabilities, looking after your own horse will give you as much pleasure as actually riding it.

Chapter 2
When your horse arrives home

- Settling in
- The five basic needs
- Avoiding mishaps
- Health matters
- Advice from "experts"

Settling in

Horses, like people, can take varying lengths of time to settle in to a new home. A horse that has experienced both busy livery stables and quiet private homes may adjust in a few days to a new environment whereas the animal that has only known one premises may take longer. It is up to you, as the new owner, to make this changeover period go smoothly.

Arrange for your horse to arrive at its new home early, on a day when you have plenty of free time. If you are keeping the horse on your own premises you will be able to observe it frequently. Avoid sudden changes to its usual routine. Use the same brand and amounts of feed as it normally has and exercise as usual. If you alter the animal's work load you have to alter the diet. Allow the horse to get to know you before introducing it to lots of new places and people.

The five basic needs

All livestock under human care have five basic needs. They are used as a guide for good husbandry and welfare codes of practice:
- Freedom from thirst, hunger or malnutrition
- Appropriate comfort and shelter
- Freedom from injury and disease
- Freedom of behaviour and movement
- Freedom from fear

Good equine management and care follows these basic principles.

Avoiding mishaps

The first hurdle, when the horse arrives, is unloading it from the vehicle. If you are inexperienced at unloading horses leave it to the person who transported the animal. Do not unload onto a public road. Position the vehicle so that the ramp is at a shallow angle to the ground and is firm. Close the yard gate! Wear a hard hat, stout shoes and gloves.

A horse that is a seasoned traveller may walk sedately down the ramp but inexperienced animals may try to jump down or rush out. It is safer to attach a long rope or lunge line to the headcollar if you anticipate trouble, or put a bridle on the horse before you drop the ramp.

Once the horse is on safe ground allow it to take in its surroundings before removing the travelling gear. Walk it into the stable which you have prepared with a thick bed. If possible put up the hay net containing hay which the vendor supplied.

Always tie up the horse using a quick release knot before you change rugs, groom and pick out feet.

Horses frequently are kicked if carelessly introduced to a new group of grazing horses. If you can graze your horse in an adjacent paddock to the other horses this will allow them to get acquainted. Some livery yards split the fields into all mares and all geldings to try to avoid injuries. Some owners like to remove the back shoes from the horses to reduce the injuries. If your horse is to mix with an established group of horses try to introduce it to one at a time. Hacking out with another quiet animal is a good introduction prior to grazing together. It is important that the field is large enough for the group and that there are no areas where an individual can be cornered. It is always a good idea to walk your horse around a new field before you turn it out. Occasionally you come across horses that will chase new animals into fences and behave in a very antisocial way. These individuals are not welcome on yards where paddocks are shared.

Before hacking on public highways it is wise to attend a road safety course and take the BHS road safety test. You should always be clearly visible to other road users by wearing fluorescent and reflective safety tabards. There is a section in the Highway Code about horse riders and how other road users should react around horses. There are hundreds of accidents every year involving horses. Sometimes roadwork is unavoidable but whenever possible avoid busy roads at peak times. It is safer to hack out in pairs especially while you are getting to know the horse.

Health matters

All horses require vaccinations to protect them from tetanus and equine flu. If your horse has no vaccination record card presume it is not vaccinated and arrange with your veterinary surgeon to start a vaccination course. Tetanus and flu combined vaccines are given by injection into a muscle. A second dose is required 4 to 6 weeks after the first, followed by a booster a year later. Usually annual boosters are given for flu and two-yearly boosters for tetanus protection.

It is advisable to deworm your horse before it grazes on new pasture or arrange with the vendor to deworm the horse a couple of days before it travels. There are three different chemical groups of wormers so you need to know which drug was last used on the horse, how much drug was used (dosage) and when it was dosed. For full details about worms and worming refer to Chapter 9.

It is important to check your horse each day for signs of good health and be aware of the early signs of disease. Often a change in manner or behaviour is the first sign that something is wrong. This means that you must be observant and spend time with your horse to become familiar with its normal behaviour. See Appendix 1 for signs of good health.

Advice from "experts"

As a novice owner you will be swamped with advice from other horsey people who all appear to know more than you! It is hard to know who to listen to. Just because someone has owned or been around horses for a long time does not mean they know it all or that they can treat ailments. Similarly, people who have driven a car for years are not always the best drivers nor can they strip an engine! If you need advice, go to the professional in that field such as a qualified riding instructor, a farrier or a veterinary surgeon. If you have a problem do not waste time getting an amateur's advice, especially on medical matters.

Chapter 3
Stabling requirements

- **Types of housing**
- **Design considerations**
- **Security**
- **Stereotypic behaviour**

Types of housing

Horses are housed in all types of buildings, from purpose built stables to converted cattle sheds, railway carriages, out houses and even glass conservatories! The stable must be safe for the horse, free from hazards, strongly constructed and properly maintained.

The American barn system has gained popularity. The horses are housed in a building with a row of loose boxes on either side of a central gangway. The horses all share the same air space so hygiene and ventilation is very important to avoid respiratory disease. The grooms are working inside the building and do not have to cope with awful weather conditions. Horses are sociable animals and this system allows them to have their own space but still have visual contact with other horses.

Design considerations

- *Size*

The stable must be large enough for the horse to walk around, lie down and get up without being injured or getting cast. The height of the roof or ceiling and the doorway are important both to prevent the horse hitting its head and for good ventilation. A metal roof tends to heat up in the summer so the stable is like an oven and causes condensation in the winter which can wet the bedding and the horse.

- *Walls*

Stone, brick or block walls can be lined with hardboard or rubber kicking boards to give a smooth finish. Wooden walls are difficult to clean and are colder in winter and warmer in summer than block walls. Walls should be checked for protruding nails.

● *Floors*

Floors should be non-slip, easy to clean and free from grids. Made to measure rubber mats of various designs are now popular as they reduce the amount of bedding required and make mucking out much easier. Farriers and veterinary surgeons have noticed that horses' hooves tend to deteriorate on this system if the stable hygiene is poor (as with any other system). Unfortunately, many people thought that by using matting they could cut corners when mucking out.

● *Bedding materials*

There are a variety of bedding materials used for horses. Straw is the traditional material and is still used. It can be eaten by the horse so it is not normally used for animals that are overweight or in hard work. It cannot be used if the horse has a respiratory allergy (COPD) to the spores in the straw. White wood shavings are a good alternative to straw. Shavings are the best bedding material for lame animals. Shredded paper is often used for ponies. Hemp can be used but has caused gut impactions (blockages) in animals that eat it. It is best to keep the horse on the bedding system it knows unless the yard has a policy on bedding material. Whatever you use, the bed should be clean, dry and deep with thick banks. This will prevent capped hocks and elbows and the horse from being cast. Deep litter beds are bad for the hooves and ammonia is an irritant to the lungs.

Manure heaps should be positioned well away from the stables and be convenient for removal by trailer.

● *Doors*

Stable doors are usually divided into a top and bottom door which can be held open by a hook. They should open outwards. Barn systems only have bottom doors of various designs. Door bolts must be animal proof so the horse cannot open them and also free from sharp edges. Gaps under the bottom door must not trap a horse's foot. The doorway width must allow the saddled horse to pass through without catching the saddle or the horse's hips on the door frame. Horses that have been injured or frightened in doorways tend to rush through them and can injure the handler.

- *Windows*

Windows must have toughened glass and removable grills. They should be high enough to allow the horse to look out but not at a height it could kick. Many horses have put their heads through unprotected windows. Windows should be positioned to allow in light and to give the animal an interesting view.

Amenities

- *Water*

The water supply needs to be convenient for the stables and protected from freezing in winter. Water can be provided in buckets or automatic drinking bowls. Automatic supplies can leak or be accidentally turned off. You cannot monitor how much the horse is drinking but they do save time and the physical effort of carrying water. Both buckets and bowls need cleaning.

- *Electricity*

Not all stables have electricity but it makes life easier especially in the winter. Electric wiring must be protected and all safety switches out of the horse's reach. Light bulbs should be encased in shatterproof covers. Wiring should be regularly checked especially in old buildings. Four legged animals are more susceptible to electric shocks.

Fittings

Mangers, hay racks and tying-up rings are the usual stable fittings. Some people prefer to use a portable manger which hooks over the bottom door or an indestructible feed bowl to feed off the floor. Hay nets are an alternative to hay racks but have to be correctly tied to a high ring to prevent the horse getting its foot in the net. Remember the net will hang lower when empty. Hay can be fed on the floor or in containers. Metal handles should be removed from buckets if the horse is playful. Fixed mangers and racks can cause accidental injuries if they are not carefully positioned.

Security

Make the stable a safe place for your horse. Do not leave mucking out tools or other equipment in the stable. Remember to close doors and yard gates to prevent straying. Horse must not be padlocked into stables in case of fire. The local police crime prevention officer will advise you on a security system. Tack and vehicles can be marked with your postal code by the police. This is a free service at present. Horses can be freezemarked, hoof branded or microchipped for identification purposes. All equines will have to be permanently identified and have a passport which conforms to EU directives by the year 2000.

Smoking should not be allowed in or around stables and it is best to put up No Smoking signs. A well maintained fire extinguisher is essential and fire buckets must be on hand. The fire brigade are always helpful with fire prevention advice. Commercial riding establishments have to be licenced and are automatically inspected for the correct safety equipment.

Stereotypic behaviour

This is the correct term for "vices" such as crib-biting, wind-sucking, weaving, box walking, swaying and so on. These repeated sequences of movements appear to have no obvious function and can annoy the owner. These types of behaviour are seen when a horse is trying to cope with a poor management system, just like the big cats pacing up and down in small cages at inferior zoos. They are the sign of a psychological problem and sometimes have an affect on the animal's physical health. Stereotypes are not seen in wild horses. You may think it is odd to mention this problem in this chapter but bad housing contributes to and can cause this behaviour. Some animals can cope better than others with poor standards of care. So how can we prevent a horse developing this problem and how do we treat it? Firstly, horses need company and freedom to move. They should not be confined for hours on end in stables, especially if they cannot see other horses. They should all be allowed the freedom of a paddock or turn out area each day as well as any ridden exercise. Horses are trickle feeders; they have small stomachs and would, in the wild, spend up to 70% of each day walking and grazing. Their diet must contain forage i.e. grass and hay to aid digestion, maintain the teeth and provide a normal activity. Many domesticated horses only have limited access to forage. Far too many horses are given concentrated diets which they do not need, instead of forage. Overstocking pastures, so limiting grass and increasing the risk of aggressive behaviour by dominant animals, can also cause stereotypic behaviour. Excessive discipline and confusing or inconsistent aids when handling or riding can also stress the horse. Improving the housing and management of horses with stereotypic behaviour is a far better option than physically restraining the animal with collars, straps and painful surgery to sever neck muscles. These methods just further frustrate the animal.

Chapter 4
Foot maintenance

- **Structure**
- **Hoof horn**
- **Daily foot care**
- **The farrier**
- **Foot balance**
- **Shoes**

Structure

All the internal structures of the hoof capsule (the wall, the sole and the frog) are included in the foot. The pedal bone (third phalanx), the navicular bone and the bottom end of the short pastern bone (second phalanx) all lie within the protective hoof capsule. The horny laminae on the inside of the hoof slot into the sensitive laminae attached to the pedal bone. The pedal bone, and therefore the weight of the horse, is suspended within the hoof capsule by the interlinking laminae. The deep digital flexor tendon which runs down the back of the leg passes over the navicular bone and inserts onto the bottom of the pedal bone. The common digital extensor tendon, which runs down the front of the cannon bone, inserts onto the extensor process of the pedal bone. The cartilages of the foot attach to either side of the pedal bone and are easy to feel above the coronary band at the heel. The fibroelastic digital cushion lies above the frog and between the cartilages. Ligaments join the bones together to form joints. Blood vessels and nerves supply all these internal structures (see diagram 1).

Hoof horn

Numerous factors affect the quality and growth rate of hoof horn:

- *Hereditary factors and the horse's state of health and diet*
Horses can inherit poor feet; debilitated and sick animals can have poor quality, slow-growing hooves. Diets low in calcium and protein result in poor horn tubule structure.

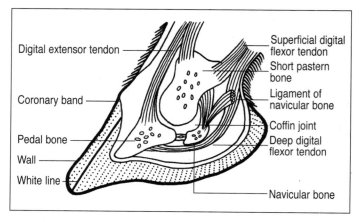

Diagram 1

Not all dietary supplements which are supposed to promote hoof growth and quality have been scientifically tested so it is best to ask your farrier or veterinary surgeon for advice before purchasing such products.

- *Environmental factors and climate*

Dirty wet beds, ammonia in urine and strong chemicals like formalin are all detrimental to hoof horn. Hoof oils, creams and tars should be avoided as they seal any excess moisture in the hoof and provide ideal conditions for infections like thrush. In hot and dry conditions the hoof dries out and may become brittle and crack, and in wet conditions the horn is saturated and the hoof loses its shape as the walls flare and the heels collapse.

- *Farriery*

As many domesticated horses live in a confined area the hoof growth rate exceeds hoof wear. Hoof wall grows about 8 to 10mm a month. The distance from the coronary band to the bearing surface of the wall at the heel is shorter than the distance to the toe. In practical terms this means that any injuries or defects at the top of the hoof wall in the heel region will grow out more quickly than those at the toe e.g. 6 months versus 9 months. The wall at the toe is thicker and older than that at the heel. Horses are shod to prevent excessive wear on their hoof wall. Their hooves need trimming at 4 to 6 week intervals.

Allowing the feet to become overlong causes distortion of the hoof capsule and lameness. The bones, joints, ligaments and tendons in the foot and higher up the limb are put under abnormal stress which can result in long-term lameness.

Your farrier will advise you on the correct trimming interval for your horse. This interval may alter from summer to winter when dietary and climatic changes affect horn growth rate.

Daily foot care

The day-to-day care of the horse's feet is the responsibility of the owner. The site of most cases of lameness is in the foot. Early recognition of a problem will mean less suffering, a quicker recovery and less expense. All horses should have their feet inspected and picked out every day. The feet should also be picked out before and after exercise. Even horses that are stabled need to have bedding material picked out of their feet to prevent diseases like thrush. Tie up the horse in a well lit area and make sure that it is standing squarely before you pick out the feet. Pick up the feet in the same sequence each day.

If you use a hoof pick with a brush on one end it is possible to remove dirt from the grooves of the frog and the white line. The wall

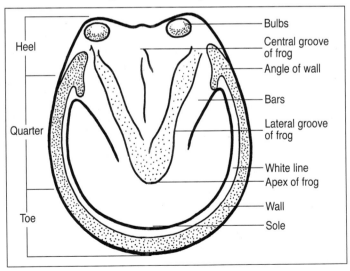

Diagram 2

should be checked for defects and cracks. Any soft or painful areas or smelly discharge will be detected. Heat in the foot may be a sign of inflammation but remember the temperature of the feet will vary throughout the day depending on the ambient temperature. If the horse is shod, the position and wear on the shoe should be noted. If the clenches (sharp end of the nails) have risen (i.e. are no longer flush with the hoof wall) they may cause injuries, the shoe will become loose and if it is pulled off, part of the wall may be torn away. As the wall grows the shoe is pulled forward, so it no longer sits on the wall at the heel but moves onto the sole, where it can cause a painful corn. Weight bearing on the sole causes bruising and laminitis. The digital pulses can be checked when the feet are inspected. Part of caring for your horse's feet involves providing a hard standing or well drained area in the pasture so that the feet do not become waterlogged and soft. Soggy feet dry quickly in a clean dry shavings bed. In very hot weather it may be necessary to soak the feet in water to prevent them drying out and becoming brittle. Clean water is a cheap dressing for feet. The oxygen permeable dressings which protect against ammonia in the bedding are preferable to hoof oil in most situations. Your farrier can advise you on which product to use, if any.

The farrier

The farrier is a qualified professional person who is often treated in a thoughtless manner by horse owners. Ideally, the farrier should be presented with a well behaved, clean, dry horse in a well lit area with a flat, clean, hard standing. Do not present the farrier with extra horses when he arrives at the yard; make sure you have booked the correct number. The horse's feet should not be oiled. Let the farrier know in advance if a horse is difficult to handle. Put a bridle on animals which tend to fidget or wander about on a headcollar. Make sure that there is a competent person to hold the horse. It is very difficult for the farrier to concentrate on the work if dogs and children are running around the yard. The farrier should not be expected to catch the horse in a field nor train it to pick up its feet! The relationship between owner and farrier will be fine if you follow these rules.

The farrier will trim the hoof and prepare it for a suitable shoe so that the horse can move freely and perform athletically. He assesses the limb conformation, the foot shape and the thickness and quality of the horn. He can then balance the foot.

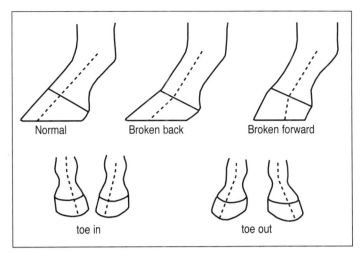

Normal   Broken back   Broken forward

toe in   toe out

Diagram 3

Foot balance

In order to assess foot balance each foot is viewed from the side, from the front and back with the foot weight bearing and how it lands in walk and trot. The ground surface is also checked for heel length. Sometimes the limb is dangled by holding it above the knee or the hock to see if the foot is in a straight line with the rest of the lower limb or if there is a deviation.

The hoof-pastern axis should be a straight line and parallel to the hoof wall at the heel and to the slope of the shoulder for the front feet. Hooves which are at too steep an angle for the pastern are club footed (broken forward) and those that are too sloping are broken backwards (see diagram 3).

The foot should appear to land flat if the inside (medial) and outside (lateral) walls are trimmed correctly i.e. mediolateral balance. This is hard to achieve in horses that do not have good limb conformation such as toe out or toe in . In the normal horse the hoof tubules at the toe are straight and parallel to those at the heels. The growth rings are the same distance apart at the toe and heels and are parallel to the coronary band and the ground surface.

The horny sole, frog and bars are trimmed to the correct thickness to avoid bruising and to allow the heels to expand when the foot is weight bearing.

When the farrier has correctly trimmed the foot he will then fit the shoe. Do not fall into the trap of waiting for the shoes to wear out or fall off before you get the hooves trimmed.

Shoes

The farrier will chose the correct shoe design and weight to suit your horse's conformation and sporting activity. Now for a word of warning. As with all other "horsey"equipment, certain shoes become fashionable but do not suit every animal There is a great maxim "if it's not broke don't fix it". If your horse is performing perfectly well with the shoes your farrier has advised, do not change things for the sake of change, you may end up with a lame animal. Be advised by your farrier, he knows your horses feet.

Shoes may be "off the peg": that is, machine made (keg) or "made to measure", that is, hand forged. Machine made shoes are cheaper but the position and pitch of the nail holes are uniform and may not correspond with the wall thickness and shape of every foot. They can be made of steel, aluminium or titanium. They are fitted either hot or cold. Hot shoeing means the shoe is heated up in the forge and then shaped on the anvil. Cold shoeing means the cold shoe is shaped on the anvil. Some horses object to hot shoeing and seem to dislike the noise and smell as the shoe is applied to the foot to check the fit. The shoe may feel hot to thin-soled animals. Metal shoes are attached to the hoof with steel nails; usually 6 nails are used. The nails should emerge about a third of the way up the wall. The ends are turned down to form the clenches which are rasped smooth. The nail heads fit the nail holes in the shoe so they all are level. Occasionally a nail may be incorrectly positioned and cause lameness. Pressure on the sensitive laminae is termed a nail bind and penetration of the sensitive tissue is a nail prick. The farrier will remove any nail that is too close to the white line. Some horses have shell-like thin walls that are difficult to nail into. Horses that will not stand still are more likely to get their feet pricked. Glue-on shoes are fitted to animals who cannot be nailed onto for whatever reason. These shoes are more expensive and the hoof wall has to be meticulously prepared to accept the fixing agent. Many designs of glue-on shoe are now available, made from a variety of materials, and are gaining popularity.

Horses with foot ailments and problem feet may have special shoes fitted such as bar shoes and wedges or pads. Surgical shoes are fitted by the farrier working with a veterinary surgeon to treat a specific ailment.

Chapter 5
Routine dental care

- **The function of teeth**
- **Eruption and wear**
- **Ageing: a matter of guesswork?**
- **Routine dental maintenance**
- **Signs of a dental problem**

The function of the teeth

The horse is a grazing animal and the teeth have an important function in the first stage of the digestion of plant material. The front teeth and the lips take the food into the mouth. The cheek teeth grind the food into small particles. The silicates in plant material are abrasive and wear down the surface of the teeth. The lower jaw is narrower than the upper jaw and as the horse chews in a circular motion it favours wear on the outside edge of the lower cheek teeth and the inside edge of the upper cheek teeth (see diagram 5). Sharp enamel points can form on the outer edge of the upper molars and the inside edge of the lower molars (see diagram 6). These sharp points can injure the cheeks and the tongue. Horses need forage, that is, grass, hay and straw, in order to wear down their teeth evenly. Animals fed on a predominately concentrate and short fibre diet do not use a wide range of jaw movement and will require more dental treatment.

Eruption and wear

The horse has two sets of teeth, the deciduous or milk teeth and the permanent set. When a foal is 9 months old it should have 24 milk teeth: 6 incisor (front teeth) and 6 premolar (cheek teeth)in the upper jaw and in the lower jaw. These are replaced by permanent teeth over the next 4 years. There are 36 to 44 permanent teeth in the adult horse. They have 6 incisors;12 cheek teeth (molars and premolars) possibly 2

Equine dentition

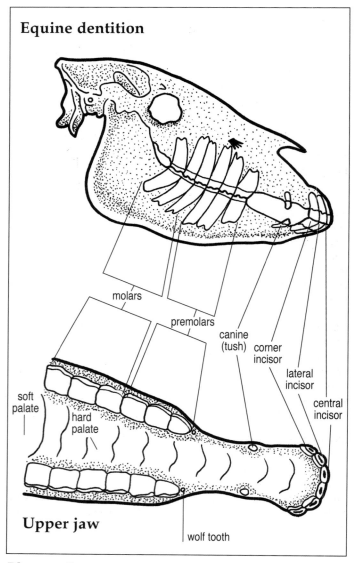

molars

premolars

canine (tush)

corner incisor

lateral incisor

central incisor

soft palate

hard palate

Upper jaw

wolf tooth

Diagram 5

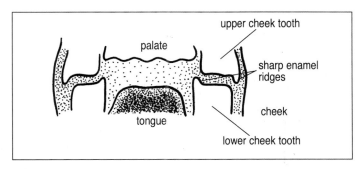

Diagram 6

canines or tushes and 2 wolf teeth in each jaw (see diagram 5). Mares do not usually have tushes. Any number of wolf teeth may be present from none to four. These teeth normally have short roots and are commonly removed as they may interfere with the position of the bit. The permanent teeth have a short root but a large reserve crown under the gum line. As the biting (occlusal) surfaces of the teeth are worn down the reserve crown continues to erupt to replace it until no more crown remains and the teeth are no longer functional.

Foals and young horses need their mouths examined to check for abnormalities which may cause problems when they are adults if they are not detected and treated at an early age.

Malocclusions (teeth out of alignment) of incisors and cheek teeth cause abnormal wear. Large hooks can form on the first upper and last lower cheek teeth and prevent jaw movement (Diagram 6). Any pain or infection will also alter the chewing pattern and if undetected will result in abnormal wear.

Ageing: a matter of guesswork?

The permanent teeth erupt at around the same age in most animals but this can depend on the breed of horse, the heavier breeds being later than the thoroughbred. Horses were traditionally "aged" by examining the incisor teeth, to see which had erupted, and the appearance of the tables (occlusal surface). Unfortunately, the amount of wear on the tables also depends on the breed and the horse's diet. The eruption of permanent incisor teeth does give a fairly accurate correlation with the actual age of the animal but as they become older ageing by teeth is less accurate and more of an informed guess. The only way you will really know the age of your horse is by documented evidence e.g. date of birth certification.

The average eruption times for permanent incisor teeth are:

Central incisors $2^{1}/_{2}$ years

Lateral incisors $3^{1}/_{2}$ years

Corner incisors $4^{1}/_{2}$ years

They are in wear with the incisors on the opposite jaw six months after they erupt.

The canines erupt at 4 to 5 years of age.

Routine dental maintenance

All adult horses need a check-up every year and those with abnormal dentition may need corrective treatment every 3 months. Just like some people, some horses may be fortunate and require no treatment at their check-ups but it is still important to have a full dental examination so any potential problem for the future will be detected.

Most horses do not object to a dental examination. Those that do object may need sedating. The horse must not be fed immediately before a check-up as the teeth will be covered in food.

The horse should be restrained on a headcollar with a loose noseband preferably in a well lit stable. The mouth can be washed out to remove food material.

Dental rasps of various shapes are used to rasp off the sharp enamel points. A full mouth speculum or gag is used to hold the jaws apart so that all the teeth can be inspected and the veterinary surgeon is not bitten. Obviously if extensive work is needed on the teeth, the horse may then be sedated and given pain relief. Sedation of horses may only be carried out by a qualified veterinary surgeon. At present dental extractions and cutting tall teeth and hooks are acts of veterinary surgery and must not be performed by lay persons. The veterinary surgeon may X-ray the horse's head if tooth root disease or sinus infection is suspected. The legislation for lay dental operators is under review and a structured training course should soon be available. This is to safeguard horses from untrained "dentists". There are a number of highly skilled equine "dentists"working with veterinary surgeons in this country but there are also a large number of cowboys, so beware.

Signs of a dental problem

Your horse may develop a dental problem in between check-ups and require treatment. Do not be tempted to feel inside the horse's mouth yourself unless you are shown the correct way, otherwise you may be accidentally bitten. Suspect a dental problem if you see any of the following signs:

- Eating slowly with altered chewing movement

- Dropping food out of the mouth (quidding)

- Pouching food in the cheeks

- Drooling

- Bad breath

- Poor condition or weight loss

- Large pieces of fibre in the faeces. Older horses with dental problems are prone to blockages in the gut

- Head shaking and abnormal behaviour when bridled. The bit and the noseband may cause the horse pain or discomfort

Chapter 6
Feeding

- **Nutritional requirements**
- **Alimentary tract**
- **Forages, concentrates and straights**
- **Supplements**
- **Simple rules for feeding**
- **Body weight and condition score**

Nutritional requirements

If you read the wrapper on any commercial feed you will see the analysis of the nutrients it contains and probably a feeding guideline. The analysis usually shows the percentages of oil, protein, fibre and starch and the amount of digestible energy. If any vitamins or minerals are present these will be listed.

The horse's nutritional requirements are: water; carbohydrates (sugar and starch); fat (oil); fibre; protein; vitamins and minerals. A horse on the correct diet will be healthy, the correct body weight and perform normal work.

- *Water is essential for the maintenance of life*

Water is obtained from two sources: drinking water and water present in food. Horses should have access to clean water at all times. Be sure to check that natural water supplies like streams have not dried up or become stagnant. Foods vary in their water content: spring grass can contain up to 90% water and hay 15%. Water is lost from the body in urine, faeces, sweat and from the respiratory tract. Exercise and high ambient temperature will increase the water requirement. Horses will lose weight if they do not have sufficient water.

- *Carbohydrate, fat and fibre are all a source of energy; that is, they provide calories*

An animal's energy requirements depend on its age, size and amount of exercise. Carbohydrates in feedstuffs are sugars, starch and cellulose. Spring grass is high in soluble carbohydrates and can cause digestion problems and laminitis. Feeding too much fat or carbohydrate, providing more calories than the body needs, will result in an overweight animal. Fat contains fat soluble vitamins A, D, E, K and the essential fatty acids are needed for good skin and coat condition.

- *Fibre is an essential part of the diet and for animals in light work at least 75% of the diet should be fibre*

Hay and grass may provide enough energy for animals in light work. Fibre is necessary for proper wear on the teeth and for healthy gut activity; after all, the horse was designed to eat forage. It takes a horse about 10 minutes to eat 1kg of concentrate pellets compared with 40 minutes to chew 1kg of long hay. Animals are kept occupied on a forage diet and are less likely to develop stereotypic behaviour.

- *Protein*

Healthy adult horses do not need a high protein diet, just enough for body maintenance, unless they are breeding. The protein could be supplied by feeding alfalfa-based forage. Feeding excess protein to the animal's requirements means more work for its liver and kidneys to convert the protein into energy and urea which is excreted in the urine. A horse on too much protein will drink more water and produce more urine. The urine will smell strongly of ammonia which irritates the respiratory tract of anyone in the stable. Feeding excessive amounts of protein to animals in hard work causes excessive heat production and may lead to heat stress. There is a risk of gut disorders and nerve irritability. Diets which are inadequate in both energy and protein result in the horse breaking down its own tissues to provide energy. This is seen as muscle wastage; and eventually the animal becomes emaciated.

- *Vitamins are needed for various body processes*

There are two groups, the water soluble and the fat soluble. The water soluble group include the B vitamins which are not stored in the body; any excess is excreted in the urine. All the B vitamins are found in grass and grains and can be synthesised by the bacteria in the horse's gut. Vitamin C is also produced in the horse's liver. Healthy horses do not need extra B and C vitamins.

The fat soluble group are stored in the liver and body fat. They are present in green forage, well made hay and cereals. In late winter the level of these stored vitamins may run out and the amount being eaten in the hay is low, so the diet may need supplementing with vitamin A and D.

Feeding or injecting excessive amounts of vitamins into horses is not beneficial and may be harmful in some cases and is certainly a waste of money.

- *Minerals play a vital role in the horse's metabolism and are an essential part of its diet*

The minerals can be split into the main group which includes calcium, phosphorus, magnesium, sodium, and potassium and the trace elements, required in smaller amounts, which are copper, zinc, manganese, iron, sulphur, cobalt, iodine, and selenium. These minerals must be fed in the correct amounts as both under and overdosing can cause diseases.

Alimentary tract

Digestion takes place in the alimentary tract. The lips and front teeth take the food into the mouth where it is mixed with saliva and ground into small particles by the cheek teeth. Any dental problems will affect this stage of the digestive process. The food is then swallowed, leaving the back of the mouth (pharynx) to be propelled down the gullet (oesophagus)

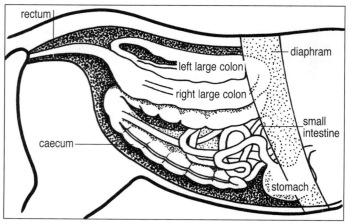

Diagram 3

into the stomach. Food sometimes causes a blockage in the oesophagus which is referred to as choke. In the stomach, different enzymes in the gastric juices start to break down the carbohydrate and the protein in the food. These partly digested contents pass into the small intestine to meet more enzymes from the pancreas and bile from the liver. The digestive process continues and the food material passes into the caecum, the first part of the large intestine. The caecum contains millions of beneficial bacteria which can break down cellulose and fibre into substances which are absorbed into the blood stream and used by the cells of the body for energy, tissue growth and repair. The types and numbers of bacteria in the caecum and colon are affected by the horse's diet. They are easily destroyed as they are very sensitive to sudden changes in diet. This can cause digestive upsets. The caecum opens into the large looped colon which also contains bacteria. Fluid is absorbed from the ingesta and faecal balls form in the colon. The faeces move along the rectum to be passed out of the anus. If you examine the faeces it is easy to see if large food particles are present. The colour and consistency will alter with diet and disease.

Forages, Concentrates and Straights

Feed stuffs can be put into three main groups:

● Forages such as grass, hay, straw, and bagged haylage, chop and chaff mixes all are fibre providers. Apart from all the nutrients they provide, they also have an important mechanical effect on the gut. They stimulate peristalsis (the movement of food along the gut);they help to remove gas and they dilute the effect of high starch diets so keeping the bacteria healthy. Horses in light to medium work can perform on a forage diet. Sometimes a supplement or forage balancer has to be added if the diet is predominantly hay and straw with little or no grass. Hay and straw can be analysed for their feed value and chemical composition. The commercial bagged products are all analysed and this is printed on the bag along with the sell by date. The values will not be accurate for products used after their sell by date.

● Concentrates or compound feeds are usually pelleted as cubes or supplied as coarse mixes. They are specially formulated for each type of performance and working horse and are fed in varying amounts with forage. There are also feeds for certain ages of animal and those with special needs. These feeds have vitamins and minerals added in the correct amounts and are scientifically balanced. If you add further supplements to these feeds you then destroy this balance. Horses only require compound feeds if the forage diet is not providing enough energy and protein, for example if they are in medium to hard work e.g. event and endurance horses.

● Straights are individual cereal grains like oats, barley and maize. These are mixed with other ingredients to make a complete feed. It needs experience and knowledge to produce a balanced diet by mixing straights and is beyond most owner's ability.

Supplements

Minerals and vitamins can be given to supplement the diet. Forage balancers are used with forage diets to provide essential amino acids, vitamins and minerals. The most common supplement is the salt or mineralised salt block or lick. There are a plethora of other supplements on the market: some are herbal, some claim to calm down animals with behaviour problems; others promote hoof quality, prevent coughs, etc. They are all expensive and most have not been scientifically tested. Many animals that are over-excitable are given too much food with too little exercise and need schooling. A lot of money is wasted by over-feeding concentrates and supplements . If you have problems with your horse's weight or exercise tolerance, most of the larger feed manufacturers have a helpline manned by equine nutritionists, who will give informed advice.

Simple rules for feeding

1. Fresh, clean water should always be available
2. Feed according to body weight and work done
3. Weigh all food and keep a record
4. Feed small amounts at regular intervals. Horses have small stomachs and are trickle feeders
5. Any changes in diet should be gradual to allow the gut bacteria to adjust
6. Only use good quality food and avoid dusty forage
7. Store feed correctly and keep utensils clean
8. Monitor body weight and condition score
9. Feed balanced rations, taking care not to overdose vitamin A, D and minerals
10. Do not feed or give large amounts of water immediately before or after exercise

Body weight and condition scoring

Horses may be weighed on a weighbridge to give the most accurate measurement. However, most owners do not have access to this equipment. There are alternative ways to calculate or estimate body weight using formulae based on body measurements or based on condition scoring and height. A number of methods give an estimated weight on a heart girth measurement, these may be accurate to within $3 - 10\%$ of the actual weight.

Condition scoring is a method used by all good stockmen to check if livestock are thin or fat or the ideal body condition. The body condition of a horse is scored by looking at and feeling three areas of the body: the pelvis, the backbone and ribs and the neck. An emaciated animal = CS 0, very thin = CS 1, lean = CS 2, good condition = CS 3, fat = CS 4 and obese = CS 5.

- *The pelvis*

The rump should be round but not so fat that there is a gutter above the tail. The bones should be felt under a layer of fat but should not be visible.

- *The backbone and ribs*

The ribs should be barely visible but easy to feel and not buried in fat. The backbone should be muscled and the spine felt on slight pressure.

- *The neck*

The horse should have a firm, muscular neck, but not a thick fatty crest, nor should the neck be scrawny. By condition scoring your horse regularly you should prevent huge fluctuations in body fat and therefore body weight. If your horse is overweight, reduce the energy intake and increase the exercise and conversely if it is losing weight and is not ill, increase the energy intake and use rugs/shelter.

In order to calculate how much and what to feed you need to know the horse's breed or type; height; weight and condition score; workload; time spent grazing and in the stable; how much feed is given at present by weight; whether the horse is rugged, clipped or has a field shelter. As a rule of thumb you need to give about 2% of body weight per day for animals in normal work, so a 500kg horse will have 10kg of food per 24 hours. If your horse is under or overweight you must calculate 2% of its ideal weight, not its present weight. This can be used as a starting point when working out a diet sheet. Remember every animal is an individual and what suits one animal may make another overweight. Heart girth measurements at weekly intervals will show any weight changes and the amount of food can be altered accordingly (see Appendix 3).

Chapter 7
How to avoid common accidents

- **Everyday handling**
- **In the stable**
- **In the field**

Everyday handling

Many accidents that happen to horses and handlers are common and should have been anticipated and avoided. Accidents are more likely to involve the inexperienced owner who may not realise how important some of the more basic practical skills are and be tempted to cut corners. This means that the owner must always be in control and not place themselves or their horse in a potentially dangerous situation. We all think "that will never happen to me" but where horses are concerned it probably will!

- *Leading the horse*

It is safer to wear a hard hat, strong boots and gloves when leading a horse, especially on a road, when it is also advisable to carry a whip to prevent the horse swinging its quarters into the traffic. See Appendix 3: BHS road safety leaflet.

The horse can be led in a headcollar, halter or bridle. Always use a bridle on a public road. Wear bright clothing so you can be easily seen by other road users; wear lights if you have to lead on a road at night. The horse can wear kneeboots and have road nails in its shoes especially in winter conditions. All equipment must be in good repair. Lead ropes may be rope or nylon; both can cause rope burns to bare hands. Some horses have not been taught to lead properly and either hang back, charge off or step on the handler. Controller headcollars can be used to train any horse to lead. Practice leading your horse in a yard or field; they should lead from either side. Always position yourself by the horse's shoulder. Never wrap a rope around your hand nor hook your fingers through headcollar rings; it is a quick way to fracture a finger.

- *Tying up*

Ideally all horses should tie up to a ring in the stable without pulling back. The ring height and rope length must be correct to prevent their front legs getting over the lead rope. Horses that play with the rope may get the lead rope clip caught on their lips or nose. Some lead ropes have safer clip designs than others. Always use a quick release knot. Horses tied to gates or fencing may pull away while still attached to the object and end up dragging it behind them or else heavy gates may fall on top of the horse. If you have to tie the horse up in a field, always tie the rope through a loop of string which will break or use a quick release clip or breakable headcollar.

- *Putting on and adjusting rugs*

The horse should be held on a lead rope or tied up while fitting or changing a rug. If the horse's rug has slipped out of place while it is in the field do not try to adjust it unless the horse is adequately restrained. If the horse gallops off before the rug has been secured it may be caught up in the rug and be badly injured. There are so many rug designs that it should be possible to find one that is a good fit, does not slip when the horse rolls and does not cause rubs.

- *Turning out into the field can be a hazardous manoeuvre*

Do not allow horses to charge out of the stable into the pasture. They may knock over the handler or slip on the way out or be injured in the gateway. Always lead them out. Train the horse to walk to the field in a calm manner and to stand quietly while you open the field gate. Take care not to catch the horse on the gate or the gate bolt as you walk through. Turn the horse to face the closed gate before you remove the headcollar. If you turn the horse out in a headcollar make sure it is a field safe design.

- *Transporting the horse*

Most accidents that happen to the horse relating to travelling do not involve other vehicles and occur while loading and unloading the animal. Some animals are injured because the vehicle has a rotten ramp or floor. Others are injured when they are left unattended tied up to the outside of the vehicle. Obviously, vehicles which are in poor repair should not be used; you would not travel in a car if your feet went through the floor. You should leave plenty of time to load and unload your horse and provide it with all the protective travelling gear.

If the vehicle has to stop suddenly or the horse slips over, leg protectors could prevent serious injuries. Lots of horses are transported without any leg protection but with a tail bandage to stop unsightly tail rubs. Do not be tempted to remove the gear before you have unloaded the horse; as it is bound to fall off the ramp! Horses may slip under the vehicle or be impaled on various bolts and other objects which protrude from the exterior of the vehicle. Check the horse at regular intervals throughout the journey and offer water. Many animals become dehydrated in transit. Travelling rugs should ensure that the animal does not sweat too much nor become cold. Travelling standing up is tiring, and tired animals are more likely to trip or fall.

In the stable

Accidents relating to stable design are covered in chapter 3. There are two common causes of injury in the stable. One happens when the horse gets cast and the other when it literally puts its foot in it! A cast horse is one that has laid down in the stable or rolled and cannot get up again because it is stuck by the wall, or the door or under a manger. Horses that roll a lot should have anticast rollers fitted and thick banks of bedding against the walls. Anticast strips can be attached to the walls. Older horses with muscle weakness or limb problems may have difficulty in rising and may benefit from rubber matting under a shavings bed. Pressure sores, capped elbows and capped hocks will develop if you skimp on bedding.

The horse may get its foot caught in a hay net, a bucket handle, in a grid or under a door or partition. Everything may look safe for the standing horse but when it lies down its legs are parallel to the ground and can easily slip under a door or through bars of a gate-type partition. Some horses have a habit of kicking the wall especially at feed times. As it is possible to fracture a pedal bone it is best to line the walls with rubber or wood.

In the field

Apart from the danger of being kicked by other horses, many accidents which occur at pasture are common. Poor and inadequate fencing causes many injuries, especially barbed wire and pig and sheep netting. Farm machinery, trailers, corrugated sheeting and jump stands with metal cups are all responsible for injuries which need not have happened as none of these objects should be left in horse paddocks. Often old cast iron baths are used as water containers and may have sharp edges. Taps should always be removed as they can all too easily be caught in headcollars. The horse can fracture its jaw trying to escape.

Ponds and streams are often the only water supply for the horse and are adequate providing the water level does not drop. Horses can become trapped in deep mud or ice when trying to reach water. They can also fall into deep ditches and need rescuing.

Do not be tempted to graze horses on lawns. Apart from the danger of eating poisonous plants, many have fallen through swimming pool covers and through the wooden lids of septic tanks.

By now you will have realised how easily horses are injured by objects in their immediate environment. See if you can spot accidents waiting to happen and take evasive action.

Chapter 8
When to seek veterinary advice

- **Register with a veterinary practice**
- **Routine health care**
- **First aid**
- **Veterinary emergencies**
- **Non-urgent veterinary visits**
- **Assisting the veterinary surgeon**
- **Second opinions and referrals**

Register with a veterinary practice

Once you have registered your horse with a veterinary practice, they will advise you on the practice protocol for visits and phone calls. Keep their phone number at home, at the stables and inside your riding hat (in case of emergencies). Most practices like their clients to give a few days' notice for routine health procedures like vaccinations. If your horse has a non-urgent injury or ailment which requires attention that day, phone at the correct time to book an appointment for that day. Emergencies obviously receive priority over non-urgent cases; so if your veterinary surgeon is late for an appointment, be patient, he is probably attending an urgent case. Many practices have a certain time during the day for clients to speak to a veterinary surgeon or nurse and if possible use this time to call. Try not to phone the veterinary surgeon at an unsociable hour to discuss routine non-urgent matters. The 24 hour service is for genuine emergencies. Remember the veterinary surgeon is human too and needs to sleep, eat, etc.

Routine health care

Your veterinary surgeon will arrange the routine healthcare for your horse. This may include:

- A worming programme

- A vaccination programme

- Routine dental maintenance

- Blood samples for a metabolic profile

- External parasite and fly control

- An annual health check-up

- Discussion of any ongoing or recurring problems

First aid

Your veterinary surgeon is the best person to advise you on first aid and what first aid equipment you should have. Every veterinary surgeon has their own ideas about the contents of a first aid kit (see Appendix 2). Your veterinary surgeon will show you how to take your horse's temperature, pulse and respiratory rate, listen to gut sounds and do a skin pinch test and a capillary refill test. See chapter 11 page 58.

Veterinary emergencies

A veterinary emergency requires immediate veterinary assistance as the animal is seriously injured or has a potentially life threatening condition.

Serious injuries are:

- Penetrating wounds to the chest, abdomen, eye, joints or tendons

- Puncture wounds that contain a foreign body like a stake or a nail

- Fractures to limbs where the bone is exposed or when the horse cannot bear weight on that limb

- Profuse bleeding from an injury or part of the body e.g. nose bleed

- Injuries to the neck or chest may cause breathing difficulties or respiratory distress and a reduction in oxygen to the vital organs

- Severe burns or collapse due to smoke inhalation

Life threatening conditions are:

- Acute laminitis where there are depressions at the coronary band

- Colics where there is severe abdominal pain

- Difficult foaling

- Collapsed or unconscious animal

- Suspect poisoning

- Difficulty in passing urine or faeces, or passing blood

- Respiratory distress ;acute allergic reaction

- High temperature (over 39°C or 102.2°F) due to fever or heat stress. Heat stroke is over 40°C or 104°F

- Exhaustion, dehydration and distress after hard exercise

If you have to cope with an emergency situation, try to be calm and give accurate details to the veterinary surgeon on the phone, not forgetting to state where the horse is. If you have a mobile phone keep in contact with the practice and ask for instructions on first aid and how to keep the horse comfortable and prevent its condition deteriorating until expert help arrives.

Non-urgent veterinary visits

Although as the concerned owner, you may feel that any illness or injury to your horse is an emergency, in fact most problems can wait a few hours without compromising the recovery of the patient and many problems do resolve themselves. Just think how long you have to wait at a local hospital A and E department. It is important to use common sense and assess the patient before dashing to the telephone. Use the signs of good health protocol (Appendix 1). You can always ring the veterinary practice for advice.

You need to arrange a veterinary visit for the same day if your horse has any of the following problems:

- Injuries which you cannot treat or are not responding to first aid. Any painful, swollen or infected wound. Wounds on horses not protected by tetanus vaccination

- Animals which are suddenly lame, obviously lame in walk or lame in more than one limb. Animals in pain, with a raised pulse rate and sweating

- No appetite or sudden loss of appetite with other signs of illness

- Fever

- Increased respiratory rate, nasal discharge, cough or swollen glands

- Diarrhoea or constipation

- Painful eye, tear overflow, eye closed, eye surface damaged

- Intense skin irritation

- Abnormal or bizarre behaviour

Assisting the veterinary surgeon

When you arrange a veterinary visit make sure that you give good directions to the horse and leave a contact phone number. If the horse is injured away from the stable or found ill at pasture the veterinary surgeon may need to examine it before moving to the stable or hospital premises, depending on the problem.

After you have made the arrangements check that you have adequate light, clean water, a clean stable for the patient, and arrange transport for the horse if need be. You may need rugs, boots or bandages. If the horse is insured check your policy. You may be required to contact the insurance company at the onset of treatment. If you think that you will be unable to handle the horse or cope with any aftercare let the veterinary surgeon know so that a nurse can assist and hospitalisation can be arranged. Not everyone is cut out to be a "nurse" (see chapter 11 page 61).

You will need a headcollar or a bridle to control the horse so that the veterinary surgeon can examine and treat the patient. You should stand on the same side of the horse as the veterinary surgeon and control it with the minimum of restraint needed in a calm but firm manner. You must focus on the horse's reactions rather than watching the veterinary surgeon! You may be asked to use other methods of restraint like holding up a foreleg, applying a twitch, or gripping a handful of skin on the side of the neck. Sometimes a small feed may distract the anxious patient. Check with the veterinary surgeon first in case sedation may be necessary. The veterinary surgeon may choose to sedate a patient that is in pain, distressed, nervous, or not well handled. It is important that no one is injured. It is not advisable to allow children to handle sick or injured horses.

Second opinions and referals

Your veterinary surgeon may wish to refer your horse to a specialist or to a clinic or hospital for further tests. The owner can also ask for a second opinion, which should be arranged with the veterinary surgeon who is already treating the horse. The second opinion veterinary surgeon needs the permission of the veterinary surgeon in charge of the case and all the medical details, prior to examining the animal. Veterinary surgeons, like doctors, often provide second opinions and as long as the correct procedure is followed no one should be offended.

The veterinary surgeon may also work with a farrier, a physiotherapist and other professionals.

Chapter 9

Worms and Worming

- **What are worms?**
- **Wormers**
- **Checking for worms**
- **Worming programmes**
- **Pasture management**
- **Redworm**
- **Tapeworm**
- **Bots**
- **Threadworm and Roundworm**
- **Lungworm**
- **Checklist**

What are worms?

Worms are internal parasites, or endoparasites, that spend much of their life cycles in the digestive tract of the horse. All horses at pasture are infected with worms, although they do not always show signs.

Worms may cause colic, blockages of the gut, weight loss, anaemia, coughing, diarrhoea and, in extreme cases, death. Both the egg-laying adult worms and the migrating larvae can damage the horse's body tissues.

Many different species of worm infect horses and their adult stages are found in different parts of the horse's body (Table 1).

Wormers

Wormers are available as in-feed granules, liquids and pastes. Pastes are squirted into the back of the horse's mouth, on to the base of the tongue. Liquids and granules can be thoroughly mixed into a small

Species of worm	Adult worm found in	Drugs used to deworm horses			
		Ivermectin	Pyrantel	Fenbendazole /Oxibendazole	Moxidectin
Large redworm	Large intestine	✓	✓	✓	✓
Small redworm	Large intestine	✓	✓	✓	✓
Roundworm	Small intestine (foals)	✓	✓	✓	✓ over 4 months old
Threadworm	Small intestine (foals)	✓	✗	*	✓ over 4 months old
Pinworm	Rectum	✓	✓	✓	✓
Tapeworm	Junction of small and large intestine	✗	*	✗	*
Lungworm	Respiratory tract	✓	✗	✗	✓
Bots	Larva in stomach (adult is a fly)	✓	✗	✗	✓
Larval stages	Migrate through various tissues depending on the species.	✓	✗	*	✓
Ovicidal		✗	✗	✓	✗
Dosing intervals		8 to 10 weeks	4 to 6 weeks	6 to 8 weeks	12 weeks

✓ = Effective at standard dose rate.   * = effective at increased dose rate.
✗ = not effective.

Table 1

feed. Always read and follow the manufacturers directions which you will find on the packaging.

The active ingredients in products used to worm horses are called anthelmintics and fall into one of the following chemical groups:

benzimidazoles	avermectins
pyrantel	moxidectin

These agents kill the parasite in different ways:

- Benzimidazoles interfere with the uptake of food by the worm.

- Avermectins cause paralysis of the worms.

- Pyrantel causes a spastic paralysis of the worms.

- Moxidectin causes paralysis of worms

The inter-dosing interval differs for the four groups of drugs.

Checking for worms

By examining faecal samples at the laboratory using a variety of tests, your veterinary surgeon will be able to tell you types of worms present, although not all worms at all stages can be identified this way. Blood tests can be used to detect anaemia and raised beta-globulins (SPE test) from gut damage caused by strongyle infection. There is also a blood test (ELISA test) specifically for tapeworm infestation used at one university veterinary laboratory. Some horses appear healthy but have a high worm burden and are contaminating the pasture with millions of eggs a day.

The faecal egg count reduction test is used to test for drug-resistant parasites. Faecal samples are taken 7 to 21 days after worming and the results are compared with a pre-worming sample. This test shows how effective the worming programme has been.

Some small strongyles (cyathostomes) have become resistant to many of the wormers in the benzimidazole group at the normal dose rate. Factors which may have contributed to this situation include underdosing and incorrect dosing intervals, as well as the short life cycle of the small redworm.

Worming Programmes

The ideal conditions needed for grass to grow (warmth and moisture) are also ideal for redworm larvae to hatch from the eggs passed out in the faeces. At temperatures over 7°C the eggs hatch and the infective third stage larvae move out onto blades of grass, where they can be eaten by any grazing animal. Most horses spend more time at grass from spring to autumn and ingest many larvae, so it is especially important to worm regularly in the spring and summer.

Choose a wormer from one of the anthelmintic groups and use it at its correct dosing interval for the entire season. The next year select a wormer from a different group so that treatment is rotated on an annual basis.

Between March and September most animals will be routinely wormed every 4 to 12 weeks depending on the worming product used that particular year. However, horses that are grazed individually, or where pasture hygiene is rigidly practised, may need fewer treatments as assessed using the results of faecal worm egg counts (FEC). Tactical worming with a wormer active against tapeworm, bots or encysted small redworms may be necessary at certain times of the year; see below for further details.

If a new horse is introduced into a premises, it should be wormed with a wormer effective against benzimidazole-resistant small redworms and stabled for at least 48 hours. By this time, the worms and eggs will have passed out of the horse. This will prevent contamination of the grazing with new worm strains that may have anthelmintic resistance.

All horses should be wormed before moving them on to new grazing. Elderly and debilitated animals should have a FEC carried out and the results of the tests should be discussed with your veterinary surgeon prior to any wormers being given.

Your veterinary surgeon will advise on a worming programme to suit your horse and management system.

Pasture management

Horses do not like to graze the areas on which they have deposited faeces and so create 'roughs' and 'lawns'. Therefore, if faeces removal is practised, more of the pasture can be grazed. Small paddocks should be cleared daily and larger areas at least twice a week during the growing season and once a week in the winter, depending on climatic conditions.

Paddocks should not be overstocked and should be periodically rested for a minimum of 5 months if this is possible. They may be harrowed during hot weather to disperse residual faecal material and expose worms and larvae to the lethal effects of sunlight. Grazing with cattle and sheep helps to reduce pasture levels of larvae.

Regular pasture larval counts, when taken into consideration with local temperature and rainfall, will show the efficacy of a worming programme and warn of potential problems.

Redworm

Small redworm

These are the most important parasite because of their ability to delay development as larval cysts within the walls of the caecum and colon in the autumn (Figure 1). In the spring, large numbers of larvae emerge from the intestine at the same time and can cause serious disease, even death. Young horses are particularly at risk. The seasonal period of highest risk is from late autumn to early spring.

Horses should be wormed in November and February with a 10% fenbendazole product licensed for use, for 5 consecutive days.

Large Redworm

These used to be the most important parasite affecting the horse's gut. The larvae migrate through various tissues and some species damage the walls of arteries which provide blood to the intestine. This causes death to the part of the bowel supplied by the blocked vessel, and results in acute colic. The incidence of large redworm infection has

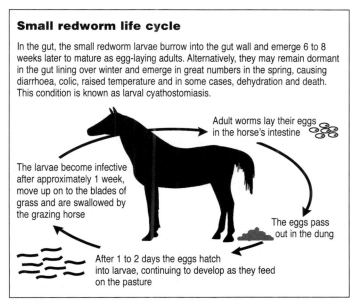

Small redworm life cycle

In the gut, the small redworm larvae burrow into the gut wall and emerge 6 to 8 weeks later to mature as egg-laying adults. Alternatively, they may remain dormant in the gut lining over winter and emerge in great numbers in the spring, causing diarrhoea, colic, raised temperature and in some cases, dehydration and death. This condition is known as larval cyathostomiasis.

Adult worms lay their eggs in the horse's intestine

The larvae become infective after approximately 1 week, move up on to the blades of grass and are swallowed by the grazing horse

The eggs pass out in the dung

After 1 to 2 days the eggs hatch into larvae, continuing to develop as they feed on the pasture

Figure 1

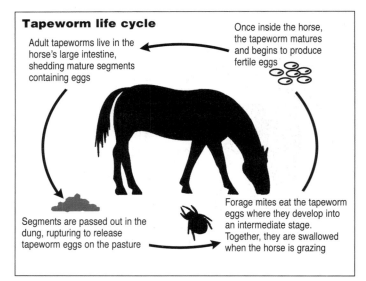

Figure 2

decreased since avermectins have become widely available, as they are effective against these larval stages, as is moxidectin.

Tapeworm

The mature tapeworm sheds segments full of eggs in the faeces (Figure 2). The eggs are eaten by the forage mite (oribatid mite). The mite lives on grassland, hay and straw. The cysticercoid stage larvae inside the mite are eaten by the horse, they then take 6 to 10 weeks to develop into egg-laying adults. The adults attach by suckers to the intestine wall at the ileocaecal junction (where the small intestine meets the caecum). They can increase the risk of spasmodic colic ileal impaction, intussusception and, in the worst case, rupture of the caecum.

Specialised faecal tests help to diagnose tapeworm infection and a blood test is also available.

Pyrantel at double the normal dose rate is the only drug available to treat tapeworm infection in equines. As part of a worming programme it is used in April and October, for horses on pasture year round and in July and October for horses stabled over the winter.

Tapeworm infection occurs within the whole of the UK.

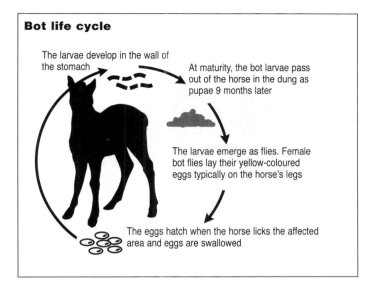

Bot life cycle

The larvae develop in the wall of the stomach

At maturity, the bot larvae pass out of the horse in the dung as pupae 9 months later

The larvae emerge as flies. Female bot flies lay their yellow-coloured eggs typically on the horse's legs

The eggs hatch when the horse licks the affected area and eggs are swallowed

Figure 3

Bots

Horse bot flies (*Gastrophilus intestinalis*) lay eggs on the legs and abdomen of grazing horses in the summer (Figure 3). They are licked off by the horse and the larvae hatch and migrate to the stomach where they stay for about 10 months before passing out in the faeces. The adult fly emerges from the pupa to complete the life cycle.

Worming with an avermectin-based or moxidectin wormer once a year, in the autumn after the first frost has killed off all the flies, is effective against bot larvae in the stomach.

Insecticides/fly repellents applied to the horse in the summer will deter flies from laying eggs. The eggs can be removed from the horse's coat with Sellotape or special bot fly combs or knives.

Threadworm and Roundworm

Threadworms live in the small intestines of young foals that become infected soon after birth, either through the dam's milk or by the larvae penetrating the skin. Foals develop an immunity to this infection after 6 months of age. Heavy infestations cause diarrhoea, dullness and loss of appetite. Ivermectin is the drug of choice for threadworm;

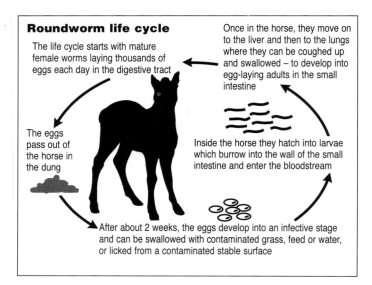

Roundworm life cycle

The life cycle starts with mature female worms laying thousands of eggs each day in the digestive tract

Once in the horse, they move on to the liver and then to the lungs where they can be coughed up and swallowed – to develop into egg-laying adults in the small intestine

The eggs pass out of the horse in the dung

Inside the horse they hatch into larvae which burrow into the wall of the small intestine and enter the bloodstream

After about 2 weeks, the eggs develop into an infective stage and can be swallowed with contaminated grass, feed or water, or licked from a contaminated stable surface

Figure 4

fenbendazole at seven times the standard dose can be used in foals from 4 weeks of age.

Roundworms are very large when mature and may cause blockages in the small intestines, failure to gain weight and emaciation (Figure 4). The female can lay millions of sticky thick-shelled eggs, which can survive for years on stable walls and floors. These eggs, containing infective larvae, are picked up by the foal. The larvae migrate via the blood to the liver and lungs. This stage causes fever, coughing and anorexia. They then return to the intestinal tract and complete their development into adults. Immunity usually develops by 2 years of age.

Mares should be wormed prior to foaling, their udders washed to remove any eggs and be provided with a clean pasture. Stables should be power cleaned and disinfected before they are used as foaling boxes. All three groups of anthelmintics are effective against ascarids (roundworms).

All the products have full instructions for use and worming advice. Owners can always seek veterinary advice if there are any problems.

Lungworm

Lungworm cause respiratory problems in adult horses and ponies, usually coughing and ill thrift. Infected larvae are passed out in the faeces of affected donkeys and foals which may themselves not show signs of the disease. The larvae are eaten by grazing horses and migrate through the blood stream to the lungs. Here, in horses, they rarely develop into egg laying adults. In the donkey, however, the larvae do mature to the adult stage and eggs are coughed up, swallowed and then passed out in the faeces.

Faecal tests for lungworm can be carried out in the donkey, but not in the horse; washings from the lungs of adult horses will usually detect infection.

Avermectins and moxidectin are the agents of choice to treat lungworm infection.

Lungworm infections have become less common both in the donkey and horse over the last few years. It is always wise to dose donkeys prior to moving them on to new pasture and to reduce the risk of infection to horses. Lungworm can survive for a long time on pasture once it has become contaminated.

Worming Checklist

- follow the instructions on the product

- use the correct dosage for the weight of animal and the worms to be removed

- use a programme to suit your management system

- remove faeces from the pasture at regular intervals

- worm all horses at the same time

- monitor results with FECs

- worm all foals and youngsters from 4 weeks old

- worm all newcomers before mixing with the herd

- worm all horses before moving onto new pasture

- wash your hands after handling medicines

- dispose of containers/packets correctly

- do not worm sick animals or those on medication

Chapter 10

Common Ailments

- ● **Digestive tract**
- ● **Lameness**
- ● **Respiratory tract**
- ● **Skin**

It is beyond the scope of this book to discuss every ailment and injury which may affect your horse. Some of the common problems can be avoided by good management and routine health care. Most ailments require early veterinary attention and advice to avoid unnecessary suffering.

Digestive tract

- ● *Dental problems*

Can be seen in horses of any age but in animals that have regular "check-ups" they will be detected and treated before they cause serious complications (see Chapter 5).

- ● *Choke*

This is when the oesophagus becomes blocked, usually with dry food material, often unsoaked sugar beet. Horses that bolt their food are prone to choke.

If the blockage is complete, no food, water or saliva can reach the stomach. The horse will be drooling food material from the mouth and nostrils and be distressed. Remove all food from the stable and phone your veterinary surgeon. To prevent choke make sure all feeds are damp and contain fibre. Remember to always soak sugar beet shreds and nuts prior to feeding.

- ● *Colic*

Is a sign of pain in the abdomen. The pain may be intermittent or continuous, and range from mild to severe. Horses with colic may look slightly uneasy and restless or be sweating and rolling depending on the level of pain. Most cases of colic involve a bowel problem which is caused by diet, worms, blockages or twists of the bowel. Some colics respond to medical treatment and others need prompt surgery if the horse is to survive. An early diagnosis is important. Horses that are rolling, pawing the ground and getting up and down will have an elevated pulse. You can take the pulse rate, check the colour of the gums and listen over both flanks for gut sounds (without putting yourself at risk). Phone the veterinary surgeon immediately with all the details. Do not give the horse any food. Do not walk it excessively as this only tires the animal. If you think it may injure itself in the stable and you have a flat paddock nearby, put it in that. Observe the horse while waiting for the veterinary surgeon and keep a record of the time between periods of pain and when urine or faeces is passed.

Reduce the risk of worms causing colic by adhering to a worming programme. Avoid sudden changes in diet, provide regular meals, provide fibre and only feed good quality horse food to prevent dietary upsets (see chapter 6).

- *Internal Parasites (worms)*

All horses at pasture are infected with worms, although they do not all show the signs. Worms may cause colic, blockages in the gut, weight loss, anaemia, coughing, diarrhoea, and even death. For details see Chapter 9, Worms and Worming.

Lameness

When a horse has pain or discomfort anywhere in its locomotory system it will alter the way it moves. The pain may occur when the horse is bearing weight on a limb or when the limb moves i.e. the joints are flexed or extended. In severe lameness it will be obvious which leg (legs) is affected but in subtle or mild cases it may be difficult to detect unless you are experienced.

Special techniques such as nerve blocks, X-rays and ultra-sound may be used by the veterinary surgeon to locate the site and the reason for the lameness.

The majority of lamenesses are caused by a foot problem. It is therefore always worth examining the foot. All cases of lameness warrant further investigation but some may be more urgent than others (see chapter 8).

The farrier will be able to advise on corns and bruises (see Chapter 4).

● *Thrush*

Is an infection of the frog and frog grooves caused by anaerobic organisms. They destroy the horn and produce a smelly black discharge. In neglected cases the sensitive tissue under the horny frog and sole is infected and the horse will be lame. It is a result of poor stable hygiene and poor foot care. Treatment will include improving the housing and management of the horse as well as specific treatment by the veterinary surgeon and farrier.

● *Laminitis*

Is a very common, serious cause of lameness in horses and ponies. Each year 1.4 % of the horse population suffer from acute laminitis and a further 1.8 % have chronic long term laminitis. It can occur at any time of year, in any number of feet and is precipitated by numerous conditions. Animals that are overweight, have long feet and are allowed free access to lush grass in spring and autumn are always at risk. Lush grass is high in soluble carbohydrates which, if digested in the large intestine, alter the gut acidity and destroy the good bacteria which digest fibre. Poisons are released from the dead bacteria into the blood stream. These disrupt the laminae and the blood flow to the capillaries which supply the sensitive laminae in the hoof. Laminitis can occur secondary to other diseases and due to concussion of the feet on hard ground. The severity of the attack depends on how many laminae are destroyed. If sufficient laminae separate, the pedal bone will move within the hoof capsule and there will be an obvious depression at the coronary band. The animal has then foundered. If all the attachments between the pedal bone and the hoof capsule separate, there is a ditch all the way around the coronary band. These animals, sinkers, require urgent specialist veterinary attention if they are to survive. If early mild cases of laminitis are not recognised or receive incorrect treatment they can founder. Laminitis is an emergency. The horse must not be forced to walk as the laminae will be torn apart. It should be transported to a stable with a deep, clean, shavings bed and given hay and water. It must not be starved but put on the correct diet. The feet should not be hosed in cold water; this will cause further constriction of the blood vessels.

Early signs of laminitis are short, pottery strides; reluctance to trot on rough, uneven ground; weight shifting from one foot to another; placing the feet down heel first; pain on finger pressure at the coronary band. Animals with laminitis have bounding digital pulses (at the fetlock). This is one of the first signs of laminitis. These pulses should be checked every day as part of foot care. The veterinary surgeon will normally give pain killers and drugs to restore the circulation to the laminae. Blood samples will show if other organs or infections are involved in causing the attack. Frog supports are used to stabilise the pedal bone. The feet of founders and sinkers are X-rayed and fitted with surgical heart bar shoes.

Animals recovering from laminitis are prone to further attacks unless they are carefully managed. Travel, stress, cold weather, worming and vaccinations can all precipitate another bout.

Chronic founder cases may become permanent cripples. This is one ailment that all owners should be aware of and try to prevent.

It is an extremely painful disease. Managing laminitic animals is hard work.

- *Foot abscesses*

Result from puncture wounds to the foot or infection gaining access through defects in the hoof wall or the white line. They are very painful until the pus has been released. Deep punctures to the middle third of the foot may damage the navicular bone or the coffin joint with serious consequences and require immediate veterinary attention.

Both the veterinary surgeon and farrier may be needed to open up an abscess tract, give medication, foot dressings and re-shoe the foot.

The owner may have to tub the foot and apply dressings (see chapter 11 page 61).

Respiratory tract

Disease of the respiratory tract are easily noticed by the owner as the horse will cough and probably have a nasal discharge. The common causes are viral, bacterial, parasitic and allergic.

- *Viral Infections*

There are many respiratory viruses. Horses with a viral infection will have a fever, cough, nasal discharge and enlarged glands in the throat. They will usually be depressed and off their food. The horse will need good nursing in a dust-free environment and complete rest for at least 1 month (see chapter 11). The veterinary surgeon should examine all coughing horses. Some cases are complicated by secondary bacterial infections. There are vaccines against equine influenza virus and equine herpes virus.

• *Bacterial Infections*

Strangles is an extremely infectious disease of the upper respiratory tract. It is spread by contact with infected animals and any discharges which contaminate the animal's environment including feed buckets, rugs, etc. The incubation period is short: only 3 to 8 days. Horses with strangles are sick: they have a high fever, a thick nasal discharge, a sore throat and swollen glands, which often burst discharging pus. The veterinary surgeon should be called out to any suspected case and the animal and its companions isolated. Strict hygiene and careful nursing is crucial. Unfortunately, there is no reliable vaccine at present against the causative bacterium *Streptococcus equi*. This disease can be confirmed by isolating the bacteria from throat swabs. Some apparently healthy animals remain as "carriers" for years and are responsible for spreading infection. Throat swabs can be used to detect these horses.

• *Parasitic infection*

e.g. lungworm and roundworm. Respiratory disease occurs in foals due to migrating large roundworm larvae and due to lungworm infections in older animals. These conditions once diagnosed can be treated successfully with anthelmintics (wormers). Donkeys with lungworm infections should also be treated to prevent pasture contamination (see chapter 9).

• *Allergic conditions*

Such as Chronic Obstructive Pulmonary Disease (COPD) are a common cause of persistent coughing and exercise intolerance. COPD is also known as broken wind or heaves.

The horse is allergic to dust and spores in hay and straw. The horse's airways will be inflamed and narrower than normal and contain mucus. Emphysema develops in animals that have repeated attacks and do not have medical intervention and management changes. The breathing rate will increase and be laboured. The abdominal muscles are used as the horse breathes out, and the "heave" line is seen. Although medication is used to treat this condition, stable management is very important in controlling it.

The horse must not have contact with the allergens (dust or spores). The stable has to be clean, well ventilated and away from straw and hay stores. Bedding should be shavings, paper or rubber mats but the horse should be kept out at pasture if possible. If hay is fed it must be soaked in water for 5 to 30 minutes and fed while it is wet. Bagged forage products can be used instead of hay in severe cases. All feed should be damp and fed at floor level. Horses suffering from viral infections may develop COPD if they are not nursed in a dust-free environment. Good stable design and good hygiene can prevent this condition occurring.

Skin

Skin disease will be seen by the owner when they groom the horse. There may be broken hair or bald patches, sores, scabs, self-inflicted wounds caused by rubbing, swelling and redness. Some conditions are very itchy and others do not irritate the horse. Many of the seasonal problems are preventable, as are skin injuries caused by poor fitting and dirty tack.

- *Seasonal problems*

Include flies, sweet itch and sunburn in the spring and summer; mud rash or fever, rain scald and lice in the autumn and winter.

- *Flies*

Are a nuisance to horse and rider. Some give painful bites while others are annoying by swarming around the animal. They spread infections and lay eggs in open wounds. They feed off body fluids from eyes, nostrils and the sheath. A variety of methods are needed to control the fly problem. Fly repellents usually contain oils that keep flies away for a few hours. Insecticidal preparations kill adult flies. Whatever you decide to use, it is best to do a spot test first. Some horses react adversely to products used on the skin. Always follow the manufacturer's instructions. Management methods include using fly fringes and veils, summer sheets, stabling the horse when the flies are most active and removing manure heaps from stable areas. Flies like water and trees, so shelters and stables should not be built in these areas.

- *Sweet itch*

Is an allergy to the bites of the *Culicoides* midge. The midges bite the neck, back and rump and this is where hair loss and self-inflicted wounds occur. Some breeds and families of horses and ponies seem to be more commonly affected. The control of this condition is similar to that for fly control. The midges feed at dusk and dawn and this is when susceptible animals are most at risk. Prevention of sweet itch means keeping the animal away from midges. When uncontrolled, this condition causes many animals to suffer.

- *Sunburn*

Horses with pink muzzles and any other unpigmented skin are prone to sunburn on these regions. They need protecting with a high factor sun screen cream or lotion. All animals need shade from strong sunlight and benefit from a shelter or stable during the hottest part of the day.

- *Mud rash, mud fever, cracked heels and rainscald*

Are caused by the organism *Dermatophilus sp.* in wet conditions. The lower limbs are infected when the skin is soaked. In mild cases there may be just a few scabs and providing the animal is kept dry it will soon recover. If the early stage is missed the legs will become swollen, painful and ooze serum. A painful secondary bacterial dermatitis will cause lameness. The horse will need antibiotics, leg dressings and stabling until it has recovered. This condition can be prevented by providing a dry hard standing in the field and a clean dry stable. Horses should not be left in waterlogged fields. Animals with very hairy limbs should be clipped so that they are easy to dry. Wet and muddy legs can be washed in warm soapy water to clean them thoroughly or just left until they are dry. Hosing with cold water only makes the legs wet and drives the mud onto the skin. A soft body brush should be used to remove dry mud. A dandy brush will damage the chapped skin.

Rainscald is seen on the topline of the horse, that is, the neck, shoulders, back, loins and rump. It is a dermatitis. Tufts of hair become matted together with serum and fall out. Large areas of skin may be involved. This condition occurs after the skin has been repeatedly soaked. It can be prevented by providing shelter and waterproof rugs in wet weather.

- *Lice*

Both biting and bloodsucking lice infest horses. They are spread by contact and by grooming equipment. Lice and their eggs (nits) are easily seen and treatment should start immediately. They cause irritation and infested horses will rub and bite themselves. All horses and equipment should be treated at fortnightly intervals until no more nits are seen. Fortunately, horse lice do not live on people!

Horses that are bathed in the late summer with anti-parasitic shampoo and treated with pour-on permethrins in the autumn are unlikely to be infested with lice in the winter. All horses should be inspected for lice at grooming time.

• Ringworm

This is a highly contagious fungal infection which can infect humans and other livestock. The veterinary surgeon will take skin samples to confirm the diagnosis. The skin lesions can vary in size and can be dry with hair loss or have scabs. The fungal spores contaminate the environment and so spread the infection. It is not difficult to treat but can be costly and very time-consuming. Every piece of tack, clothing, equipment and the stables have to be cleaned and treated with an antifungal preparation. The infected animal should be isolated while it is treated. The incubation period is 1 to 2 weeks and all in contact animals should be closely inspected during this period.

• Tumours

The sarcoid is the most common skin tumour. This can spread locally and be difficult, time-consuming and expensive to treat successfully. They vary in appearance and growth rate and do not always require treatment. If they are rubbed by tack and so prevent the horse being ridden, they have to be treated. It is a gamble to buy a horse with sarcoids. Any skin growths should be examined by a veterinary surgeon, who can take a sample (biopsy) to identify the type of tumour.

Chapter 11

First aid

> ● **Checking vital signs**
> ● **Wounds**
> ● **Nursing the horse**
> ● **Medicines**

Checking vital signs

● *T. P. R.*

It is useful to know your horse's normal temperature, pulse and respiratory rate to use as a reference at times of illness. Practice doing these tests while the horse is standing quietly in the stable.

● *Temperature*

You need a clinical thermometer, Vaseline and a piece of cotton wool. Tie up the horse. Remove the thermometer from its case and shake it so that the mercury is below the scale, and lubricate the bulb with Vaseline. Stand close to the side of the hind quarters and raise the tail. Slide the bulb of the thermometer through the anus into the rectum to lie against the rectal wall. Do not prod the wall with the thermometer and do not push it into a ball of faeces. Hold it in place for a minute and then remove, wipe clean and read the temperature off the scale. Clean the thermometer in cold antiseptic solution, dry it, shake it and place it back in the case.

The normal rectal temperature is 37.6 – 38.2°C or 99 – 100.5°F.

● *Pulse rate*

To take the pulse rate you need a watch with a second hand. Find the facial artery. It is close to the skin surface on the bottom jaw. Locate the tubular vessel on the lower edge of the jaw with your finger tips. Alter the finger pressure until you feel the pulse. Count the number of beats in 15 seconds and multiply by 4 to obtain the pulse rate.

The normal resting rate is 32 to 40 per minute depending on the size, age and fitness of the horse.

- *Respiratory rate*

Breathing is barely noticeable at rest in the healthy horse. Stand back from the horse and watch the movement of the rib cage or the flanks. Count the number of breaths in or out over 15 seconds and multiply by 4. Normal respiratory rate at rest is 8 to 16 per minute.

- *Gut sounds*

Listen over the right and left flanks of the horse to hear gut sounds. The amount of noise depends to some extent on when and what the horse has been eating. The absence of gut sounds and increased sounds are significant when monitoring colic cases.

- *Skin pinch test*

The skin at the point of the shoulder is lifted between finger and thumb, squeezed and released. In the healthy animal the skin should go back into place immediately. In dehydrated animals the tent of skin remains for over 2 seconds.

- *Capillary refill tests*

The gums should be pink and moist. Press on the gum above one of the top incisor teeth to blanch it . The colour should return immediately you remove your finger. A delay suggests a reduction in blood volume or blood pressure due to shock, haemorrhage or dehydration.

Wounds

All wounds, however, small should be carefully checked. The type, position, amount of bleeding, presence of foreign material and the degree of pain associated with the injury should be noted (see chapter 8).

- *Types*

Wounds are classified as follows:

- Bruises are caused by bleeding under the skin due to a kick or blow. The skin surface is intact. Large bruises (haematomas) may need veterinary care. Cool packs or crushed ice can be applied over a protective layer of gamgee to the bruise to control bleeding.

- Abrasions involve the surface of the skin and hair loss. They are painful but do not bleed a lot. They can be caused by scrapes on a hard surface, rope burns and badly fitting tack.

- Incised wounds have clean straight edges, bleed liberally but are not very painful as there is little bruising. They are caused by sharp objects. They are often sutured (stitched).

- Lacerated wounds are usually contaminated;they have jagged edges as there is tissue loss; they bleed freely, and other deeper tissues like muscle and bone may be involved. They require veterinary attention as soon as possible.

- Punctures are caused by a sharp penetrating object which may damage deep structures beneath the surface wound. There are often bacteria, splinters and dead tissue in the tract.

However trivial a wound may appear, the veterinary surgeon must attend any unvaccinated animal to give tetanus antiserum (antibodies). Routine vaccination for tetanus is recommended. Tetanus is an extremely unpleasant and usually fatal disease and may occur after an injury.

- Management of wounds always involves the owner and often the veterinary surgeon, too. The horse must be calmly restrained, preferably in a well lit area. Moving will increase the bleeding. Heavy bleeding has to be controlled before the wound can be assessed and assistance sought. Ideally, a sterile dressing (e.g. melolin) is placed over the wound and pressure applied; in an emergency, use any clean piece of material. The cleanliness can be sorted out later when the bleeding has stopped. Leg wounds can be pressure bandaged to control bleeding. Do not be tempted to remove the bandage as this will dislodge any blood clots. Let the veterinary surgeon do this.

  Small wounds that are not bleeding can be cleaned with dilute antiseptic solution after you have washed your hands. Place KY gel into the wound before cutting the hair from the wound edges. This is easy to wash off and stops any hair falling into the wound. Do not hose wounds as this forces debris into the wound and waterlogs the tissues. Plastic indoor plant spray bottles can be filled with dilute antiseptic and used to clean wounds. The skin below the wound can be protected with Vaseline to prevent any discharges from sticking (see Appendix 2: First aid kit).

● *Tubbing the foot*

Puncture wounds to the foot can be cleaned by tubbing the foot in a bowl of warm water. This usually requires two people. The horse is stood in the yard. A large bowl is put close to the foot and the leg is lifted. The bowl is pushed into position and the foot is placed in the centre of the bowl. The assistant picks up the opposite leg to prevent the horse stepping out of the bowl. Warm water is carefully added until the foot is submerged. Some horses will put their foot into a bowl containing water but others kick it over. A shallow bowl is easier to use than a bucket. Tubbing the foot softens the hoof horn and makes it easier to pare. This also encourages abscesses to burst and is an alternative to using poultices.

● *Dressings and bandages*

Limb wounds should be covered with a non-stick dressing, cotton wool or gamgee secured in place with a conforming bandage. There is a definite skill to bandaging. Incorrectly applied bandages can cause damage. Tubular stockinette is an alternative to bandages, as are velcro fastened boots. Disposable nappies are useful as foot dressings and easy to apply. They can be protected with waterproof barrier boots. Bandages protect wounds from further injury or contamination and support the injured tissue. Trivial wounds and those in awkward places may not need bandaging. Lotions, creams, powders and sprays can be used as directed by your veterinary surgeon.

Nursing the horse

Whenever possible, ill or injured animals are nursed at home in surroundings they know and by the people they trust. Sometimes the facilities or the expertise needed cannot be provided by the owner and in this case the horse will be hospitalised at the veterinary clinic.

Sick and injured animals need to be stabled. They need frequent attention not only to monitor progress but also to keep the bed clean and supply small nutritious feeds. Shavings are the preferred bedding, especially for lame horses. Water buckets should be changed frequently and discarded food removed from the stable. Make sure the horse can reach the food and water.

The veterinary surgeon's instructions should be followed, including advice on diet and exercise.

Horses with limb injuries may be on box rest. This means that the horse remains in the stable at all times until the veterinary surgeon is satisfied that it can be walked out in hand. The horse can be given ad lib hay to prevent boredom and groomed and massaged to keep its muscles toned. It may need support bandages on the uninjured limb(s) and frog supports on feet that are taking extra weight. The feet should be picked out twice a day and digital pulses and temperature monitored. The horse may need a rug.

Lightweight Thermatex rugs are warm but allow any sweat to be wicked away from the skin. Put the horse's bridle on when walking out in hand and pick a time when the yard is empty and quiet.

Nursing horses with infectious diseases carries with it the extra responsibility of preventing the disease spreading to other animals. The isolation box should be at least 400 yards away from any other stables and not on a road or track that other horses are using. The nurse needs waterproof protective clothing or overalls, boots and gloves which can be disinfected on leaving the stable. All equipment for mucking out and grooming should be kept apart and disinfected after use. Discarded bedding can be burnt or bagged. Any discharges from the eyes or nostrils can be cleaned with damp cotton wool and Vaseline applied to the surrounding area. Sick animals need to be quietly observed and allowed to rest. They do not need visitors, who, however well intentioned, may spread the infection.

A daily record chart to include the food eaten, water intake, urine and faeces passed, TPR and any medication given are useful to monitor progress.

Medicines

- *Storage*

Most medicines should be stored in a cool, dry, dark, locked cupboard. Any out-of-date or part-used bottles should be correctly disposed of in the clinical waste. A record should be kept of all medicines used with dates, patient's name and amounts given. A horse should not be given a drug that was prescribed for another patient. Children should not handle horse drugs, nor be responsible for giving medicine.

- *Administration*

Veterinary surgeons mostly ask owners to give medicines to horses that can be given by mouth. This can be as a powder, paste or pills.

They can be added to a small feed, put into a sandwich or a cored apple or squirted into the back of the horse's mouth.

It is important to give the entire course of treatment and make sure the whole dose is swallowed. Some medicines are dosed twice a day (BID) i.e. every 12 hours or three times a day (TID) i.e. every 8 hours. Inform the veterinary surgeon if the patient has not received the medicine so that it can be given by another route. Drugs can be given by injection into a muscle (I/M) or vein (I/V) or under the skin (S/C). Animals with COPD may be given drugs to inhale through a face mask. Skin ailments may be treated with washes, lotions or creams. Always wash your hands before and after handling medicines.

● *Regulations*

Regulations governing many medicines used on horses are changing because of EU law. Horses are used for meat in other member states so they cannot be given certain drugs. Horse owners in the UK may be asked by their veterinary surgeon to sign a certificate stating that their horse will not enter the food chain before they are allowed these medicines e.g. the painkiller phenylbutazone.

Appendices

Appendix 1

Signs of good health

- *Behaviour, manner and attitude*

The healthy horse is interested in its surroundings and looks alert with ears pricked. It should have a healthy appetite and show no reluctance to eat. It should pass well formed faeces.

- *Posture, stance and movement*

The head and neck should have the full range of movements needed to graze and self groom. The limbs should bear equal weight at rest and when the horse moves, the strides should be regular and even. The feet should be in good condition.

- *Body condition and weight*

The ideal condition score is 3 (on a scale of 0 to 5), that is, the body has a thin layer of fat under the skin so the animal is the correct body weight for its height and type.

- *Skin and hair*

The skin should be supple and free from swellings, scabs and sores. The coat should lie flat and shine. The mane and tail should be full with no sign of broken hair.

- *Eyes and nostrils*

The eyes should be bright and wide open with no discharge or tear overflow on the face. The nostrils should be free of discharges and not be flared at rest. The breath should smell sweet.

- *Vital signs should be within the normal ranges*

See chapter 11.

Appendix 2
Contents of a First aid kit

Ask your veterinary surgeon to advise you on which items to include in the kit. You may wish to have a first aid kit at the stable yard and a kit to use if travelling to shows, etc.

It is best to carry a few essential items when out on a hack eg. money, phonecard, mobile phone, non-adherent dressing, antiseptic swab, conforming bandage, piece of string, Swiss army type knife.

These items should fit inside a small plastic bag. Write the veterinary surgeon's phone number and your own name and number inside your riding hat.

The first aid kit is for emergency use. The contents should be kept in a clean container in a cupboard in the tack room:

A bowl

A plastic measuring jug

Plastic freezer bags (many uses)

Kitchen roll or paper towel

Curved scissors

Tweezers

Thermometer

Jar of Vaseline

Bottle of liquid soap

Antiseptic eg. Hibiscrub or Pevidine to be diluted with water to clean wounds

Large roll cotton wool

Roll gamgee

Bandages: Self adhesive 10cm eg. Vetrap

Tubular eg. Tubigrip

Roll of electric insulating tape

Set of stable bandages and elastic exercise bandage

Dressings for wounds eg. melolin sheets 10 X 10cm, Opsite spray, Intrasite gel, Allevyn

Disposable nappies (foot dressing)

Barrier boot

Animalintex poultice

Cold pack (or thermos to carry crushed ice)

Eye wash or ointment

Large, 60ml, dosing syringe

Fly repellent

Milton to clean equipment

Twitch

Note pad and pencil

It is useful to have a pair of wire cutters and a large pair of pliers in the tack room.

Appendix 3
Suggested further reading

B.H.S. Welfare leaflets on health care/general management

B.H.S. Road Safety Leaflet

Colour Atlas of Diseases and Disorders of the Horse
by Derek Knottenbelt

Explaining laminitis and its prevention by Robert Eustace

Farewell, Making the right decision; HSA

Feeding and Watering by Teresa Hollands

Horse Owner's Guide to Lameness by Stashak

Poisonous plants in Britain; MAFF Ref 161

Soundness in The Horse by Peter Gray

Veterinary notes for horse owners; revised by Peter Rossdale

Appendix 4
Useful addresses

Association of Chartered Physiotherapists in Animal Therapy
Moorland House
Salters Lane
Winchester
Hants
SO22 5JP
Tel: 01962 863801

British Equine Veterinary Association
Administration Secretary
5 Findlay Street
London
SW6 6HE
Tel: 0171 6106080

British Horse Society
Stoneleigh Deer Park
Kenilworth
Warwickshire
CV8 2XZ
Tel: 01926 707700

Farriers Registration Council
Sefton House
Adam Court
Newark Road
Peterborough
PE1 5PP
Tel: 01733 319911

Laminitis Clinic
Mead House Farm
Dauntsey
Chippenham
Wiltshire
Tel: 01249 890784

Royal College of Veterinary Surgeons
Belgavia House
62–64 Horseferry Road
London SWIP 2AF
Tel: 0171 222 2001

Society of Master Saddlers
Kettles Farm
Mickfield
Stowmarket
Suffolk
Tel: 01499 71164

Appendix 5
Points of the horse

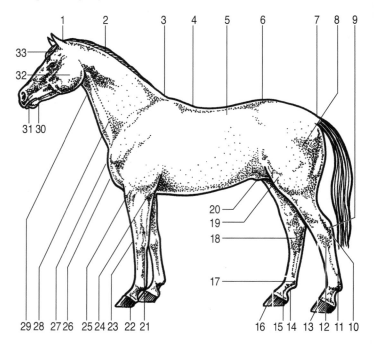

1. Poll	12. Hind cannon bone	22. Coronary band
2. Crest	13. Fetlock joint	23. Knee
3. Withers	14. Heel	24. Elbow
4. Back	15. Pastern	25. Forearm
5. Loins	16. Hoof wall	26. Brisket
6. Croup or Rump	17. Ergot	27. Point of the shoulder
7. Dock	18. Chestnut	28. Jugular groove
8. Buttocks	19. Stifle joint	29. Windpipe
9. Point of the hock	20. Sheath	30. Chin
10. Hock joint	21. Fore cannon bone	31. Muzzle
11. Flexor tendons		32. Cheek
		33. Forehead